Love Songs from the Movies

Wise Publications
London / New York / Paris / Sydney / Copenhagen / Berlin / Madrid / Tokyo

Exclusive Distributors:

Music Sales Limited
8/9 Frith Street,
London W1D 3JB, England.

Music Sales Pty Limited
120 Rothschild Avenue,
Rosebery, NSW 2018, Australia.

Order No. AM965734
ISBN 0-7119-8331-3
This book © Copyright 2002 by Wise Publications.

Compiled by Nick Crispin.
Music arranged by Derek Jones.
Music processed by Paul Ewers Music Design.
Cover design by Michael Bell Design.
Printed and bound in Malta by Interprint Limited.

Cover image: Moulin Rouge!
Video and DVD are available now to buy from
Twentieth Century Fox Film Corp.

Also available from Wise Publications:
Songs From Baz Luhrmann's Moulin Rouge!
All the tracks from the album arranged for piano, voice and guitar.
Order No. AM972763

Your Guarantee of Quality
As publishers, we strive to produce every book to
the highest commercial standards.
This book has been carefully designed to minimise awkward
page turns and to make playing from it a real pleasure.
Particular care has been given to specifying acid-free,
neutral-sized paper made from pulps which have not been
. elemental chlorine bleached.
This pulp is from farmed sustainable forests and was produced
with special regard for the environment.
Throughout, the printing and binding have been planned to
ensure a sturdy, attractive publication which should
give years of enjoyment.
If your copy fails to meet our high standards, please inform us
and we will gladly replace it.

www.musicsales.com

AGAINST ALL ODDS
(TAKE A LOOK AT ME NOW)

Words & Music by Phil Collins

Slow rock

1. How can I just let you walk a-way, just let you leave with-out a trace? When I stand here tak-ing ev-'ry breath with you; ooh, you're the on-ly one who real-ly knew me at all.

(Verses 2 & 3 see block lyric)

Verse 2:
How can you just walk away from me
When all I can do is watch you leave?
'Cause we shared the laughter and the pain
And even shared the tears.
You're the only one who really knew me at all.

Verse 3:
I wish I could just make you turn around
Turn around and see me cry.
There's so much I need to say to you
So many reasons why.
You're the only one who really knew me at all.

ALL LOVE CAN BE

Words by Will Jennings
Music by James Horner

AS TIME GOES BY
Words & Music by Herman Hupfeld

Moonlight and love_ songs, nev-er out of date, hearts_ full of pas-sion,
jeal-ous-y and hate; wo-man needs man and man must have his mate, that
no one can de-ny. It's still the same old sto-ry, a
fight for love and glo-ry, a case of do or die.___ The

world will al-ways wel-come lov-ers as time goes by.

by.

ANGEL
Words & Music by Sarah McLachlan

1. Spend all your time wait-ing _____ for that sec-ond chance, _____ for a
(Verse 2 see block lyric)
break that would make_ it O. K. _____ There's al-ways some rea-son to feel

not good e - nough___ and it's hard at the end___ of the day.___

___ I need some dis - trac - tion. Oh,___ beau - ti - ful re - lease.___

Me - mo - ries seep from my veins, and may be emp - ty, oh,

weight - less and may - be I'll find some peace to - night.___ In the

arms of_____ the an - gel, fly a - way_____ from here._____

From this dark, cold_____ ho - tel room and the

end - less - ness that you__ fear. You are pulled from the

wreck - age of your si - lent_____ re - ve - rie._____ You're in the

Verse 2:
So tired of the straight line
And everywhere you turn
There's vultures and thieves at your back
And the storm keeps on twisting
You keep on building the lies
That you make up for all that you lack
It don't make no difference
Escape one last time
It's easier to believe
In this sweet madness
Oh this glorious sadness
That brings me to my knees.

In the arms of the angel *etc.*

THE BEAUTIFUL ONES
Words & Music by Prince

1. Ba - by, ba - by, ba-
(Verses 2 & 3 see block lyrics)

- by,

what's it gon - na be?___

vi - sion in one's mind.＿

The beau - ti - ful ones＿ al - ways smash the pic - ture.

Al - ways, ev - 'ry - time.＿

Mm.＿＿＿＿＿

D.%. al Coda

Coda

beau - ti - ful ones＿ u al - ways seem＿ 2＿＿

me? I got-ta know, I got-ta know,_ do u want

me? Ba-by, ba-by, ba-by, lis-ten 2 me.

Play 9 times ad lib.

Drums

Verse 2:
Baby, baby, baby
Can't u stay with me tonight?
Oh, baby, baby, baby
Don't my kisses please u right?
U were so hard 2 find
The beautiful ones, they hurt u everytime.

Verse 3:
If I told u, baby
That I was in love with u
Oh, baby, baby, baby
If we got married would that be cool?
U make me so confused
The beautiful ones, u always seem 2 lose.

BECAUSE YOU LOVED ME

Words & Music by Diane Warren

26

COME WHAT MAY
Words & Music by David Baerwald

29

there by your side.___ Storm clouds may ga - ther and stars may col - lide. But I love you_____ un - til the end of time. Come what___ may,_____ come what___ may,_____ I will love you_____ un - til my dy - ing day. Oh come what___ may,_____ come what_

may, I will love you, will love you.

Sud - den - ly the world seems such a per - fect place.

rit.

Come what may, come what may,

I will love you until my dy - ing day.

33

FOR ALWAYS

Words by Cynthia Weil
Music by John Williams

HOPELESSLY DEVOTED TO YOU

Words & Music by John Farrar

Moderate 2

1. Guess

mine is not the first_____ heart bro-ken,_____ my

(Verses 2 & 3 see block lyric)

Verse 2:
I know I'm just a fool who's willin'
To sit around and wait for you.
But, baby, can't you see
There's nothin' else for me to do.

Verse 3:
My head is sayin' "Fool, forget him."
My heart is sayin' "Don't let go.
Hold on to the end."
And that's what I intend to do.

I WILL ALWAYS LOVE YOU
Words & Music by Dolly Parton

Slow, freely

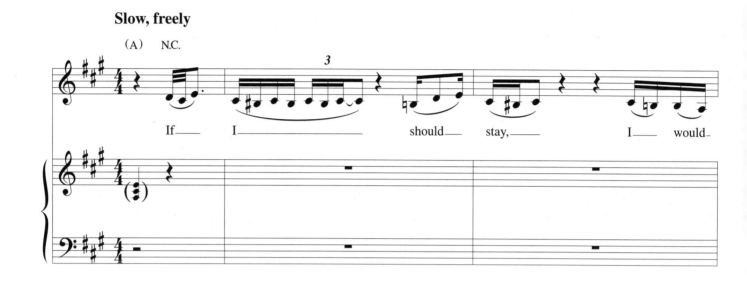

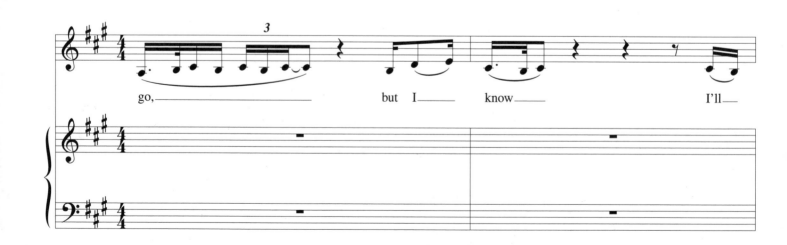

think of you___ ev-'ry step___ of the way.___

a tempo (♩= 62)

And I___ will al - ways

love you,___ I___ will al - ways

poco accel.

love you,___ you,___ my

45

47

I WILL FIND YOU
Words & Music by Ciaran Brennan

1. Hope is your___ sur - vi - val.
(Verse 2 see block lyric)

Cap - tive___ path___ I lead.___ No mat - ter

where you go I will find you,

Con pedale

w' yu ha le w' yu ga i sv____ ha le

w' yu. Hal - le - lu - ia. No mat - ter where you

go I will find you, if it

takes_____ a long, long time.

Verse 2:
Nachgochema anetaba
Anachemowgan
No matter where you go I will find you
In a place with no frontiers
No matter where you go I will find you
If it takes a thousand years.

(EVERYTHING I DO) I DO IT FOR YOU
Words by Bryan Adams & Robert John Lange
Music by Michael Kamen

no love___ like your love,___ and no___ oth - er could give___

more___ love. There's no - where_____ un - less___ you're___ there all the

time,_____ all the way,___ yeah._____

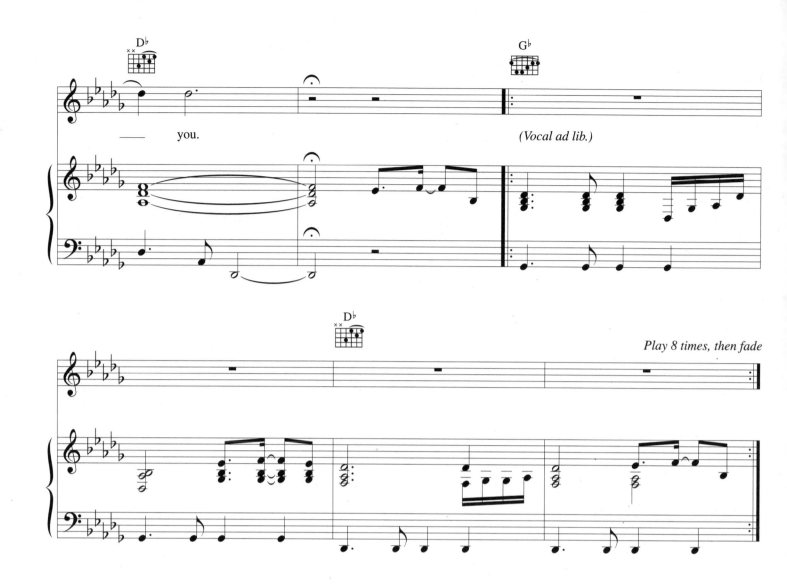

you.

(Vocal ad lib.)

Play 8 times, then fade

Verse 2:
Look into your heart, you will find
There's nothin' there to hide.
Take me as I am, take my life
I would give it all, I would sacrifice.
Don't tell me it's not worth fightin' for
I can't help it, there's nothin' I want more.
You know it's true, everything I do
I do it for you.

I'M KISSING YOU

Words & Melody by Des'ree
Music by Tim Atack

IT MUST HAVE BEEN LOVE

Words & Music by Per Gessle

but it's ov - er now, _____ it must have been _____ good _____

but I lost it some - how. _____ It must have been _____ love _____ but it's ov - er now, _____

from the mo - ment we touched _____ till the time had run out.

Make be _____ but it's ov - er now, _____ it's where _____ the wa -

Verse 2:
Make believing we're together
That I'm sheltered by your heart.
But in and outside I turn to autumn
Like a teardrop in your palm.

And it's a hard winter's day
I dream away.

It must have been love but it's over now
It was all that I wanted, now I'm living without.
It must have been love but it's over now.
It's where the water flows,
It's where the wind blows.

IT HAD TO BE YOU

Words by Gus Kahn
Music by Isham Jones

LOVE IS ALL AROUND
Words & Music by Reg Presley

1. I feel it in my fin-gers,   I feel it in my toes.—
(Verse 2 see block lyric)

The love that's all a-round me

and so the feel - ing grows.___ It's

writ - ten on the wind, it's ev - 'ry - where I go,___

so if you real - ly love me, come on and let it show.___

You know I love you, I al - ways___ will, my mind's made up by the

way that I feel.___ There's no be - gin - ning, there'll be no___ end,___ 'cause

on my___ love___ you can de - pend.___

2. I

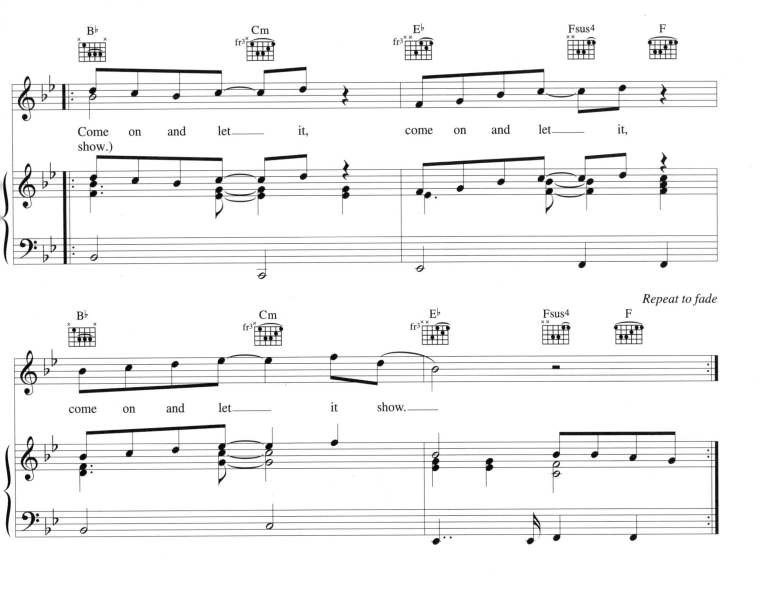

Come on and let——— it, come on and let——— it,
show.)

Repeat to fade

come on and let——— it show.———

Verse 2:
I see your face before me
As I lay on my bed;
I cannot get to thinking
Of all the things you said.
You gave your promise to me
And I gave mine to you;
I need someone beside me
In everything I do.

A LOVE BEFORE TIME

Words & Music by James Schamus, Tan Dun & Jorge Calandrelli

be - fore _____ time. _____

D.S. al Coda

CODA

die, _____ but the light _____ that I _____

_____ see _____ in _____ your eyes _____ will burn there

LOVE SONG FOR A VAMPIRE
Words & Music by Annie Lennox

♩ = 60

1. Come in - to _____ these arms _____ a - gain _____ and
(Verses 2 & 3 see block lyric)

Cue 2° + 3° only

lay your bo - dy down. _____

The rhy - thm of _____ this trem - bling heart, is beat - ing like a _____

⊕ Coda

free.

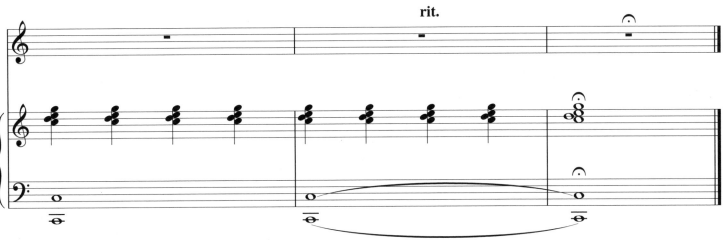

Verse 2:
Once I had the rarest rose
That ever deemed to bloom
Cruel winter chilled the bud
And stole my flower too soon
Oh loneliness, oh hopelessness
To search the ends of time
For there is in all the world
No greater love than mine.

Verse 3:
Let me be the only one
To keep you from the cold
Now the floor of heaven is laid
With are stars brightest gold
They shine for you
They shine for you
They burn for all to see
Come into these arms again
And set this spirit free.

NOT OF THIS EARTH
Words & Music by Robbie Williams & Guy Chambers

Verse 2:
Not of this earth
She came walking down my lane
I've learnt to laugh again
Like a moth to a flame
Not of this earth
Not surprised we're unashamed
She's gonna have to change her name
Then we'll know that we're the same.

She is not of this earth
And I believe we've seen the worst
If I ever leave this world
You will have a song to sing
So you'll know what you're worth.

Verse 3:
As verse 1.

PELAGIA'S SONG (RICORDO ANCOR)

Music by Stephen Warbeck
Words by Paco Reconti

a tempo

-cor in so - gno con me, il tuo vol - to tra i miei sguar - di ru - ba - ti al

mon - do sol' per te. Io sa - rò per te un fiu - me di

ne - ve bian - ca che si scio - glier - rà al so - le dei tuoi oc - chi di pri - ma - ve - ra.

Guar - da - mi an - co - ra. Ri - cor - do an cor' in fon - do al

SHE
Words by Herbert Kretzmer
Music by Charles Aznavour

sings, ___ may be the chill that au-tumn brings, ___ may be a hun-dred diff-'rent

things ___ with-in the mea-sure of a day.

2. She ___ may be the beau-ty or the beast, ___ may be the fa-mine or the
(Verse 3 instr. Verse 4 see block lyric)

feast, ___ may turn each day in-to a hea-ven or ___ hell.

She— may be the mir-ror of my dreams— a smile re-flect-ed in a stream, she may not be what she may

seem, in-side her shell.

She— who al-ways seems so hap-py in a crowd,— whose eyes can be so pri-vate and so

proud,— no-one's al-lowed to see them when they cry.

She — may be the love that can-not hope to last, — may come to me from sha-dows of the

D.%. al Coda

past — that I'll re-mem - ber till the day I die.

✠ *Coda*

She, she, — she.

Verse 4:
She may be the reason I survive
The why and wherefore I'm alive
The one I'll care for through the rough and ready years.
Me, I'll take her laughter and her tears
And make them all my souvenirs
For where she goes I've got to be
The meaning of my life is she, she, she.

SHOW ME HEAVEN

Words & Music by Maria McKee, Jay Rifkin & Eric Rackin

1. There you go, flash-ing fe-ver from your eyes.
(Verse 2 see block lyric)

Hey babe, come ov-er here and shut down tight.

I'm not de-ny-ing we're fly-ing a-bove it all,

hold my hand_ don't let me fall_ you've such a-ma-zing

grace, I've ne-ver felt this way.___ Oh,_____

show me hea-ven,_ co-ver_ me,___

leave me breath-less.__ Oh,_____

show me hea - ven please.

If you know what it's like_ to dream a dream,_

ba-by hold me tight and let_ this_ be._ Oh,_____ Oh,_____

show me hea - ven,_ co - ver_ me,___

Repeat and fade

leave me breath - less._

Oh,_____

show me hea - ven please.

Verse 2:
Here I go, I'm shaking just like the breeze.
Hey babe, Ineed your hand to steady me.
I'm not denying I'm frightened as much as you.
Though I'm barely touching you,
I've shivers down my spine, and it feels divine.

Oh, show me heaven, *etc.*

TAKE MY BREATH AWAY

Words by Tom Whitlock
Music by Giorgio Moroder

Watch-ing ev-'ry mo-tion in ___
Watch-ing, I keep wait-ing, still ___
Watch-ing ev-'ry mo-tion in ___

___ my fool-ish lov-er's game; ___
___ an-tic-i-pat-ing love, ___
___ this fool-ish lov-er's game; ___

on this end-less o-cean, fi-
nev-er hes-i-tat-ing to ___
haunt-ed by the no-tion some-

TURN BACK TIME

Words & Music by Soren Rasted, Claus Norreen, Johnny Pederson & Karsten Delgado

1. Give me time to rea-son, give me
(Verse 2 see block lyric)

time to think it___ through.___

Pass-ing through the sea-

stay.

The nail re-minds me I was there.

The

nail re-minds me I was there. If on-ly I could

Verse 2:
Claim your right to science
Claim your right to see the truth,
Though my pangs of conscience
Will drill a hole in you.

I've seen you coming like a thief in the night
I've seen it coming from the flash of your light
So give me strength to face this test of mine.

119

THIS YEAR'S LOVE

Words & Music by David Gray

1. This year's love had bet-ter last;_____ hea - ven knows, it's high
(Verse 2 see block lyric)

time.___ I've been wait-ing on my own too___ long.___

And when you hold me like you do___ it feels___ so___ right,___ oh now,___

I start to for-get how my heart gets torn when that
(Verse 3 see block lyric)

hurt gets thrown; feel-ing_____ like I can't_____ go on._____

dream in - side my soul, when you kiss me on that mid - night street, sweep me

off my feet, sing - ing ain't this life so sweet?

This year's love had bet - ter last.

This year's love had bet - ter last.

To Coda ⊕

D.%. al Coda
(As 2º)

Verse 2:
Turning circles and time again
It cuts like a knife, oh now
If you love me I got to know for sure
'Cause it takes something more this time
Than sweet, sweet lies, oh now
Before I open up my arms and fall
Losing all control
Every dream inside my soul
When you kiss me on that midnight street
Sweep me off my feet
Singing ain't this life so sweet.

Verse 3:
'Cause who's to worry if our hearts get torn
When that hurt gets thrown?
Don't you know this life goes on?
Won't you kiss me on that midnight street
Sweep me off my feet
Singing ain't this life so sweet?

TRY A LITTLE TENDERNESS
Words & Music by Harry Woods, Jimmy Campbell & Reg Connelly

1. Oh, she may be wea-ry, and young girls, they do get wea-ry wear-ing that same old_____ shab-by dress._____

But when she gets wea - ry _____   try

a lit - tle ____ ten - der - ness. ____

♩ = 100

Fan - dan - go.

2. You
(Verse 3 see block lyric)

know she's wait - ing,   just an - ti - ci - pat - ing ____ the

things_____ that she nev - er, nev - er, nev - er, nev - er pos - ess - es, yeah.__

But while__ she's there wait - ing with - out them,

try_____ a lit - tle ten - der - ness.__

That's all you got - ta do. This is for you.

Verse 3:
You won't regret it, no, no
Young girls, they never forget it
Love is their only happiness
But it is all so easy
All you gotta do is try a little tenderness   *etc.*

UNCHAINED MELODY

Words by Hy Zaret
Music by Alex North

Oh, my love, my dar - ling, I've hun - gered for your touch a long, lone - ly time. Time goes by so slow - ly and time can do so much, Are you still

UP WHERE WE BELONG

Words & Music by Jack Nitzsche, Will Jennings & Buffy Sainte-Marie

Who knows what to-mor-row brings;___ in a
Some hang on to "used to be,"___ live their

world, few hearts sur-vive? All I know is the
lives look-ing be-hind. All we have is

way I feel;___ when it's real, I keep it a-live.___ The
here and now;___ all our life, out there to find.___

WE HAVE ALL THE TIME IN THE WORLD

Music by John Barry
Words by Hal David

WHEN YOU SAY NOTHING AT ALL

Words & Music by Don Schlitz & Paul Overstreet

1. It's a-maz-ing how you can speak right to my heart,
(Verse 2 see block lyric)

with-out say-ing a word

truth in your eyes say - ing you'll — nev - er leave — me. The touch of your hand says you'll catch

— me wher - ev - er I fall. —

You — say it best when you say no - thing at all. —

when you say no - thing at all. —

me where-ev-er I fall.

You say it best when you say no-thing at all.

(You say it best when you say no-thing at all.)

(You say it best when you say)

146

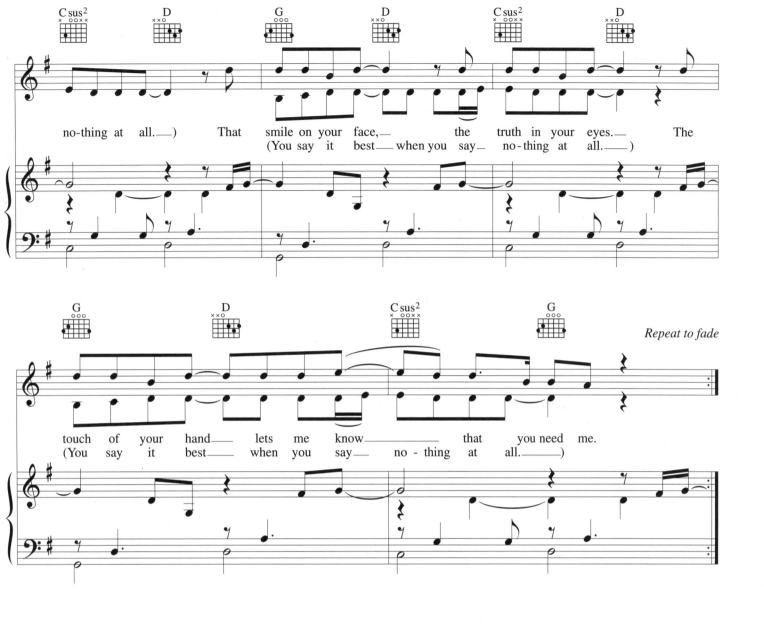

Repeat to fade

Verse 2:

All day long I can hear people talking out loud
But when you hold me you drown out the crowd
Try as they may they can never defy
What's been said between your heart and mine.

The smile on your face *etc.*

YOU MUST LOVE ME

Music by Andrew Lloyd Webber
Lyrics by Tim Rice

Cer - tain - ties dis - ap - pear

(2° see block lyric)

what do we do___ for our dream to sur - vive,

how do we keep___ all our pas-sions a - live as we used to do?___

Deep in my heart I'm con - ceal - ing

things that I'm long-ing to say, scared to con-fess what I'm

feel — ing fright-ened you'll slip a-way, you must love

me, you must love

To Coda ⊕

me.

D.%. al Coda ⊕ **Coda**

You must love me.

2° lyric
Why are you at my side?
How can I be any use to you now?
Give me a chance and I'll let you see how
Nothing has changed.
Deep in my heart I'm concealing
Things that I'm longing to say,
Scared to confess what I'm feeling
Frightened you'll slip away,
You must love me.

151

YOUR SONG

Words & Music by Elton John & Bernie Taupin

I real-ly mean,_ yours are the sweet-est eyes_ I've_ ev-er seen._

And you can tell ev-'ry-bo-dy_____ that this is your song,_ it may be quite_ sim-ple but

now that it's done._ And you can tell ev-'ry-bo-dy this is your song,_

it may be quite sim-ple but now that it's done._ I hope you don't mind, I hope you don't mind

A LOVE SO BEAUTIFUL
Words & Music by Roy Orbison & Jeff Lynne

11/04 (53204)